HYMNS FOR FINGERSTYLE GUITAR

By Doug Young

www.dougyoungguitar.com

ISBN 978-0-9896349-3-9

To download audio recordings, visit
http://bit.ly/FingerstyleHymns

Rev 4.04.23

ACKNOWLEDGEMENTS

Thanks to:

My mother, Janet Young, for her collection of hymnals from which I drew most of these songs.

Teri Young, my wife, for editing and and supporting this project.

Dedicated to the memory of Terry Wilhelm

Cover photo:

Hymnals from Janet Young's collection along with an 1890's Washburn guitar owned by Steve Baughman.

TABLE OF CONTENTS

FORWARD

This book grew out of a need. Recently, I was asked to play during several funerals, with the request being to "just play some hymns." When I began looking for material, I found a wealth of wonderful arrangements for fingerstyle guitar, but none of them were going to work for me in this situation. Naturally, I had only a few days' notice, so I wasn't going to learn and memorize complex arrangements, no matter how beautiful they were. Even the simplest arrangements I found were many pages long, and I didn't want to be turning pages during a funeral service, the way I would if I tried to read the music rather than memorize it. I also realized that in this setting, the focus wasn't on me, or how clever or complex the music was. I just needed to play appropriate music for the occasion that helped set the mood and that didn't detract from the service. Uncomplicated, melodic arrangements would be a plus.

My solution forms the basis of this book – my own arrangements that are simple, almost "sketches" of an arrangement. What I decided I needed was a type of book known as a "fake book" in jazz circles – but for hymns – and designed for solo fingerstyle guitar. Jazz fake books are typically limited to just chord names and perhaps melody. I wanted a bit more than that – basically easily-playable arrangements with no complicated parts, and designed to be extended on the fly.

These were my goals:

1. The hymns must be in standard tuning to avoid retuning during a service.

2. The arrangements must be simple enough to read during the performance with minimal preparation and no memorization.

3. No page turning required.

4. The music should fall comfortably in first position, with simple fingerings.

5. The hymns must be in guitar-friendly keys. In most hymnals, these songs are written in keys like Bb, Eb, Ab and so on. If you need to play in other keys for a singer or to match another instrument, consider using a capo.

6. The arrangements should be as minimalist as possible, but lend themselves to simple embellishments during performance. (We'll discuss this in more detail in the section on "How to Use This Book".)

7. Each arrangement, although simple, should sound musical when played exactly as written. I often try to leverage simple re-harmonization to complement and enrich the song when played as a solo instrumental, without straying from the simple and reverential character of the hymn.

I hope you find these arrangements useful for your own needs, whether you play them exactly as written, or take them as a starting point for your own enhanced arrangements.

Doug Young

ABOUT THE RECORDINGS

Audio recordings of the hymns in this book can be downloaded from:

http://bit.ly/FingerstyleHymns

For these recordings, I generally follow the approaches outlined on page 9. I generally play each tune the first time exactly as written, so you can follow along and hear how the arrangement is supposed to sound if you just follow the music exactly. Then I continue with one or two additional verses, improvising embellishments. In some cases, I also improvised introductions or endings for the songs.

Some of the recordings use a capo to change the key. I did this just to add a little variety – playing a group of hymns all in the same key can start to sound monotonous after a while. You should be able to add or move a capo easily between songs during a performance, to add some variety. You might also want to try any or all of these hymns in different keys by using a capo to see if you like the resulting change in texture. Most of the arrangements fall within a small range of frets on the guitar, so you should be able to try higher capo positions (5th or 7th fret) with no problem.

The improvised sections are not written out – that would defeat the entire goal of the book. I elaborated on the written arrangement on the fly during recording, and probably would not (or could not) play the song exactly the same way again. However, I briefly describe how I approached each song in the notes on the page before each hymn. I encourage you to explore your ideas, not necessarily to work out the embellishments I added.

Where I thought it might be useful or instructive, I have written out some of my improvised introductions or endings in the notes before each song. These segments provide some examples of techniques that can be used to add some interest to the hymns. But again, I'd just take these as seeds for your own ideas!

HOW TO USE THIS BOOK

The arrangements in this book can be used in several ways. They can be played exactly as written, either as a solo instrumental, or to accompany singers. They can also be used as the basis of your own interpretations, which you can either work out in advance, or "improvise" variations on the fly. By improvise, in this context, I don't mean playing guitar solos like you would in jazz or rock music; I mean simply taking liberties with the arrangement, adding embellishments and variations on what is written.

Let's briefly explore each of these scenarios: playing as written, backing up singers, and embellishing the hymns to create longer arrangments, and also touch on adding introductions and endings.

Playing Instrumentally As Written

I've designed these arrangements to be fairly easy to play - as easy as I could make them while still sounding musical. The music is written in two staffs with both standard notation and tablature – a fairly common convention these days. The chord names and shapes are also provided above the staff. The chord shapes shown often indicate a subset of the full chord, reflecting the fingering being used in the arrangement at that point.

Each arrangement consists of only a single pass through the song, which will be quite short, in most cases. You can repeat the song as many times as you like. In songs that have pickup notes, I have followed a non-conventional notation technique of showing the pickup notes in the last measure in parenthesis. This is meant to indicate that you can play them when repeating the tune, but skip them on the final time through. Usually this would be shown as first and second endings, but that creates more complex-looking notation, and I wanted to avoid any distraction or complexity as much as possible.

The interpretation of these hymns is entirely up to you. When hymns are sung by a congregation, they are often played and sung fairly stiffly, often with an almost march-like tempo and feel, since that makes it easier for groups of singers to follow the tempo and stay together. When performing instrumentally, you can play with more feeling and expression, playing slower, or even varying the tempo or playing more rubato.

Supporting Singers

These arrangements should work well as a way to support singers, either for a performance or a congregation. You could play the music as written, which is usually most effective when supporting a congregation singing. This mode is similar to how most church pianists play when leading a congregation. If you are supporting a smaller group performance, you might decide to skip playing the melody, and rely primarily on the chord changes as a way to accompany the others.

In churches I have attended, pianists or organists usually started songs by playing the last phrase as an introduction, establishing the tempo – and also reminding the congregation of the song. If you want to use this approach, either to support singers, or even as an introduction for an instrumental version, I have marked the start of the last phrase with a ✻ symbol. This allows you to use the section from the ✻ to the end, and then begin playing the

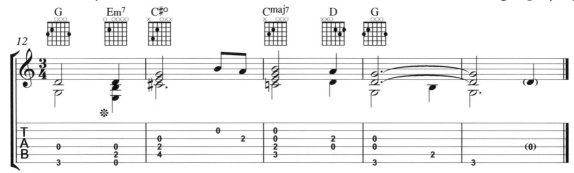

song from the beginning. For example, here are the final bars of Amazing Grace:

You could start the introduction with the last note of measure 12, playing either the full chord, or just the top melody note, and then play to the end.

In many cases, it would make sense to have the introduction end on the V or V7 chord (D or D7 in the key of G, G or G7 in the key of C, and so on). This isn't indicated in the arrangement, but is always an option you can introduce on your own. For example, you could play an introduction of Amazing Grace as follows (again, starting from the note marked with the ✻):

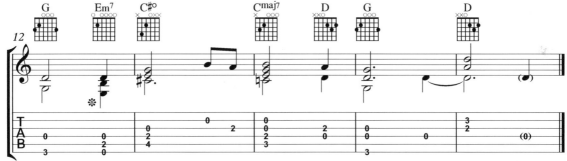

If you are performing with others and have time to rehearse, you might consider creating a less cookie-cutter introduction. Introductions can be as simple as playing arpeggios in the appropriate time signature and tempo over the first chord. For example, for Amazing Grace, you could playing something like this (the D at the end of the final measure is the pickup note into the melody):

Any number of simple chord progressions within the key make good candidates for introductions. A few ideas include:

- Play I-V7 (G-D7 in the key of G). Play the I chord as long as seems appropriate – perhaps 3 measures – then end on the V7 chord to set up the beginning of the song. For example, an introduction to Amazing Grace could be something like this:

- Play I-IV-I-V7 (G, C, G, D7 in the key of G). This is just a variation of the above idea, but in this case, we're adding the IV chord for some extra color. For example, here's another possible introduction to Amazing Grace:

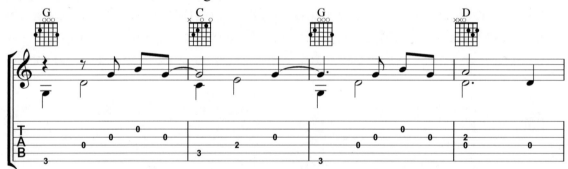

- Play I-vi-ii-V (G, Em, Am, D7 in the key of G). This is a common chord progression in popular music and sounds a bit more sophisticated that the simple I-IV-V7 chords. Using this approach, you could create this introduction to Amazing Grace:

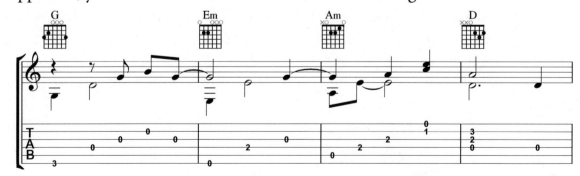

These are just a few ideas; feel free to explore and create your own introductions.

Playing Instrumentally With Variations

I primarily use these songs as solo fingerstyle instrumentals, which is how they are performed in the accompanying sample recordings. When performing solo, you have a lot of flexibility in how you interpret the songs. You can pick the tempo and add your own stylistic elements. These arrangements should be simple enough that you can easily add arpeggios, passing notes, additional bass notes and so on, as you see fit, even when you are basically sight-reading the songs.

Here's what I typically do to turn these simple arrangements into full performances:

1. Add an introduction (see the discussion above about accompanying singers for some introduction ideas).

2. Play the song as written the first time through. I keep it as simple as possible. The most important thing in a service (especially a funeral service) is to not make distracting mistakes. Played expressively, these arrangements should sound good exactly as written.

3. On the second time through the song, I start to add some arpeggios and extra chord notes in any spots where there is space. I don't want to obscure the melody, (and it is important to know the melody!), but some simple natural additions will make it sound like a more sophisticated arrangement. Less is more in this situation; it doesn't take a lot to enhance the song.

4. Having played two times through, if I am feeling confident of the song, I will take more liberties on a third pass. One approach is to vary the timing of the melody slightly – think of how a good singer might perform the song. I may slightly anticipate melody notes, and may also delay bass notes.

5. Finally, when I have played long enough, I add an ending. Endings can be as simple as slowing down – a ritard – on the final phrase. Or I might play a simple chord progression, like I-IV-I at the end. So if the song ends on a G, I'd play G, C, G. Another approach is to use a "tag" ending, where you repeat the final phrase. To do this effectively, you might slightly ritard as you approach the final measure, then go back the point indicated by a ✳ in the music (usually four bars from the end), and play that phrase again, with a more dramatic ritard on the closing measure.

More specific ideas for each song are included in the notes on the page before the song, but these are always just suggestions. Use your own ideas to extend or embellish the songs in any way that sounds good to you!

Let's look at a few ideas for introducing variations, using the first line of Amazing Grace as an example.

The following example demonstrates adding some simple arpeggios as additional accompaniment. As long as you finger more or less complete chord shapes while playing the tune, you should be able to easily add these accompaniment patterns in many places. The key is to look for places where there is space, and to never forget to bring out the melody. Notice the delayed bass note on the C chord. This is another way to vary the accompaniment and make the arrangement sound more complex and interesting.

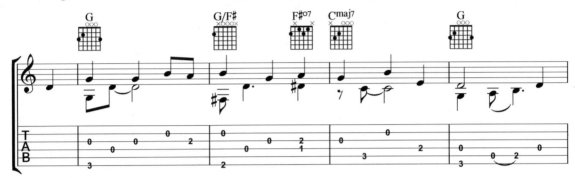

Or consider another example. In this case, I'm taking some liberties with timing, slightly anticipating the initial melody note in each measure. This example also adds some additional bass notes, but keeps the accompaniment simpler than the previous example, because the intent of this technique is to emphasize the melody and give it a more vocal-like quality.

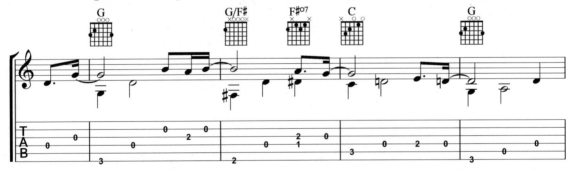

Here's another approach, using more or less continuous eighth-note arpeggios, weaving the melody notes in with the accompaniment.

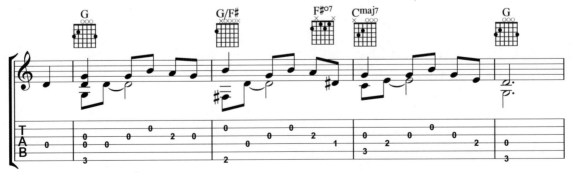

Creating Endings

Let's look at a few examples of how you might add effective endings to a hymn when performed as an instrumental, using Amazing Grace as an example. In this first example, we'll create an ending by simply slowing down in the final two measures, holding the last three melody notes and chords a bit longer.

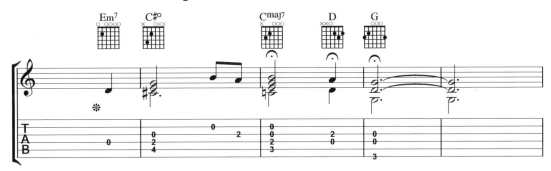

The following example extends the final G chord, by playing a simple arpeggio pattern over G, then C, then back to a final G chord.

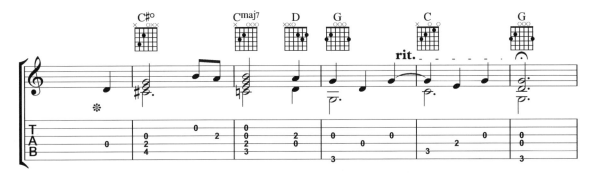

As a final example, lets look at one way to create a "tag" ending. Here, we play the last phrase, but move to a C chord, which is held out slightly longer for effect, then return to the final phrase (marked with a ✽), and play through to the end. For the ending, we'll extend the timing of the final three melody notes and chords dramatically, holding each for a full three beats.

HYMNS BY KEY

ABIDE WITH ME

Words: Henry Francis Lyft (1847)
Music: William Henry Monk (1861)

Abide with me; fast falls the eventide;
The darkness deepens; Lord with me abide.
When other helpers fail and comforts flee,
Help of the helpless, O abide with me.

Abide With Me is a poem written in 1847 by Henry Francis Lyft, a Scottish Anglican priest as he was approaching his death, inspired by a phrase spoken by a friend who had died earlier. The hymn is usually sung to the melody of "Eventide", which was written by William Henry Monk in 1861.

Performance Tips and Comments

This arrangement is in the key of C, and uses mostly first position chord shapes. I tend to mix Cmaj7 and straight C major according to what sounds right to me; these chords are somewhat interchangeable. You could use major seventh voicings for nearly all C chords, except for the final chord, where the top C is the melody note.

One potentially awkward spot occurs in measures 3 and 6, where the melody goes up to a 5th fret A, harmonized by an F chord. An F major 7th chord would sound nice here, but I found it was easier to play smoothly by fingering the chord as shown, playing only the 1st, 3rd, and 4th strings.

Introduction Suggestions

For a standard introduction, play the final four bars, starting at measure 13, optionally going to a G or G7 at the end to set up the verse.

Ending Suggestions

You could repeat the last four bars, starting at measure 13 or just the final 2 bars, starting with the pickup note to measure 15, to create an ending. If playing the song as an instrumental, also consider holding the half notes in measure 15 four beats each into the final chord.

Sample Recording

The performance on the recording is very simple, with no introduction. I just played the tune as written one time, then repeated it again, with some added arpeggios on the longer chords. The tune ends with a slight ritard.

ABIDE WITH ME

Henry Francis Lyte/William Henry Monk
Arr. Doug Young

AMAZING GRACE

Words: John Newton (1779)
Music: Traditional

Amazing grace! How sweet the sound
That saved a wretch like me.
I once was lost, but now am found,
Was blind but now I see.

Amazing Grace is one of the best-known hymns in the world; it has been recorded thousands of times, and it is estimated that it is performed millions of times each year. Like many hymns, it was originally sung to various melodies, but has come to be associated with the melody known as "New Britain," which combines two traditional English folk melodies. Amazing Grace has achieved popularity among folk musicians, and has been recorded by Joan Baez, Judy Collings, and others. It was performed at Woodstock, and even sung by President Obama during a televised eulogy. It is often played at funeral services.

Performance Tips and Comments

This arrangement is quite simple and should be easy to play. The melody is so well-known that you can embellish it substantially. Think about how a singer would phrase the song, and feel free to vary the timing or phrasing to make it "sing."

Introduction Suggestion

The final phrase, starting with the Em7 in measure 12 to the end serves as a typical introduction. A sequence of I-IV-I-V (G, C, G, D7) would also work nicely. Or try a chord progression of G, G/F#, Em, D, with a descending bass line, something like this:

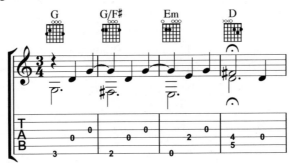

Ending Suggestions:

A simple chord progression of G, C, G would work nicely as an ending. You could also use the descending bass line suggested above for the introduction: G, G/F#, Em, D, and then ending on a G.

Sample Recording

For the recording, I used a capo on the 2nd fret, to give the tune a bit of a lift – so the song sounds as if it is in the key of A. A capo is worth exploring with any of these hymns; using a capo not only changes the key, but changes the character and texture of the sound. The recorded introduction is a simple arpeggiated riff based on a first position G chord, walking down to Em. In the second verse, I introduce a few simple arpeggios on the longer chords, but otherwise keep things fairly simple. Between the second and third verses, I repeat the G down to Em riff, similar to the intro, as a sort of interlude. For the final verse, I focused on anticipating the melody notes, similar to the example on page 10. For the ending, I return again to the G descending to Em idea, leading into a repeat of the final four bars. I end by arpeggiating the final G chord, ending on a high G on the 3rd fret, 1st string.

AMAZING GRACE

John Newton
Arr. Doug Young

A Mighty Fortress is Our God

Words: Martin Luther (1529)
Music: Martin Luther

A mighty fortress is our God,
A bulwark never failing:
Our helper He, amid the flood
Of mortal ills prevailing.

A Mighty Fortress is Our God is one of the best-known hymns written by Martin Luther. The lyrics are based on Psalm 46. The song was, of course, written in German originally and was known as Ein Feste Burg.

Performance Tips and Comments

The timing of this song is a bit irregular. Some versions are written with changing time signatures, or sometimes with no time signature at all. In this arrangement, I have written the song in 4/4 time, but indicated holds (⌒) at the end of most phrases. You can ignore these, or play them the way you feel them. I tend to hold these chords for three beats (effectively making those measures 6/4 time) If you are performing solo, you can experiment with the timing however you like, but you will want to be more consistent if you are accompanying singers. The key of C results in the melody to this hymn lying fairly low on the guitar, with the final note being a 5th string, 3rd fret C. I harmonized this melody note with the open 6th string E, which isn't ideal, but works as long as you emphasize the C melody note.

Introduction Suggestions

The final two measures, including the pickup note on the fourth beat of measure 14, makes a good introduction if you are setting up the song for singers.

Ending Suggestions

The final two measures could be repeated as a tag ending. You might consider playing the full final C chord, plucking the strings so that the C on the 1st fret, 2nd string, is on top. For example:

Sample Recording

On the recording, I started with the first verse as written, and then took a few liberties with timing and added occasional extra accompaniment notes here and there on the second verse. To end the song, I played an Am instead of the final C chord before repeating the last phrase, starting with the last note of measure 14. Instead of playing the final low C as written, I played a first position C chord, and played an ascending arpeggio, sliding up to a high C on the 8th fret at the end.

A MIGHTY FORTRESS IS OUR GOD

Martin Luther
Arr. Doug Young

BE THOU MY VISION

Words and Music: Traditional

Be thou my vision, O Lord of my heart;
Naught be all else to me, save that thou art
Thou my best thought by day or by night,
Waking or sleeping, thy presence my light.

Be Thou My Vision is the English version of an old Irish poem, "Bí Thusa 'mo Shúile". The melody is also an old Irish tune, "Slane". The two were first combined and published in 1927.

Performance Tips and Comments

This tune is in 3/4 time, in the key of G, and lies comfortably in first position. The melody is rhythmically quite simple, with sequences of straight quarter-notes, sometimes repeated at the same pitch, so try not to play it too stiffly. You might try to add rolling eighth-note arpeggios wherever possible to create a sense of motion.

Introduction Suggestion

The last four measures work as a typical introduction when accompanying singers. As an instrumental, standard turnarounds in G, such as G, Em, Am, D7 should work well to introduce the tune.

Ending Suggestions:

Repeating the final four measures, with a ritard, works well for this tune.

Sample Recording

On the recording, I start with a simple arpeggiated introduction, starting on G, walking down to an Em, followed by C, then D. Here is the intro on the recording:

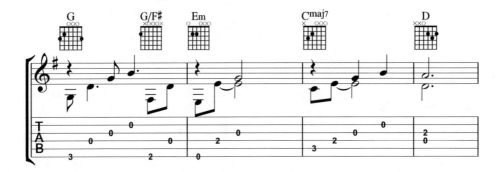

After the initial verse, played as written, I introduced a few additional chord tones (arpeggios) and introduced some slight variations in phrasing. On the third verse, I focused on delaying the bass notes in many chords. I simply played the melody, without the indicated chord or bass note, and then played the bass note an eighth note later. To end the tune, I substituted an Em9 chord for the final G chord, and then repeated the final four bars, with a ritard into the final notes.

This trick of creating a false cadence by playing the relative minor at the end before going to a tag ending works with many tunes. But if you are performing multiple songs, be careful not to use this technique on every song, as it will become predictable.

BE THOU MY VISION

Traditional
Arr. Doug Young

BLESSED ASSURANCE

Words: Fanny Crosby (1873)
Music: Phoebe Knapp

Blessed assurance, Jesus is mine!
O what a foretaste of glory divine!
Heir of salvation, purchase of God,
Born of his Spirit, washed in his blood.

Blessed Assurance was created when Fanny Crosby, a prolific author of hymns, added the lyrics to a melody that had been previously written by her friend, Phoebe Knapp.

Performance Tips and Comments

This tune is in 9/8 time, which may seem challenging, but it simply feels like 3/4 time, with a triplet feel. You can count it as **1**,2,3 **2**,2,3 **3**,2,3. The chord changes go by fairly quickly in some places, so make sure you can move between them smoothly. To enhance the arrangement, you can try to add eighth-note arpeggios – with the triplet feel – between the longer-held chords.

Introduction Suggestions

A standard introduction option would be to start on the pickup notes at the end of measure 14. You could also use a longer phrase, starting with the pickup notes at the end of measure 12. In either case, consider going to a D7 chord to set up the verse. A simple triplet finger picking pattern over a G chord would also be effective.

Ending Suggestions

The pickup notes at the end of measure 14 and final two measures would make a nice tag ending.

Sample Recording

The sample recording introduces the song with a simple triplet picking pattern over G, C, G, then ending on a D. The first verse is played as written, while the second adds triplet accompaniment patterns during the longer chords. For the ending, I walked down from the final G, to F#, landing on the Em at the end of measure 14 to pickup the last phrase again.

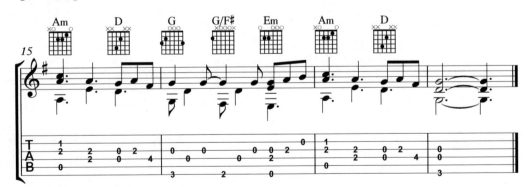

BLESSED ASSURANCE

Fanny Crosby/Phoebe Knapp
Arr. Doug Young

COME THOU FOUNT OF EVERY BLESSING

Words: Robert Robinson (1758)
Music: Anonymous

Come, thou fount of every blessing,
Tune my heart to sing thy grace;
Streams of mercy, never ceasing,
Call for songs of loudest praise.

Robert Robinson wrote the lyrics to this popular hymn, which were later set to the melody of a tune known as "Nettleton" (author unknown). Nettleton first appeared as a hymn named "Hallelujah" in 1813.

Performance Tips and Comments

This is a fairly straightforward tune in 3/4 time, and using mostly I, IV, and V chords (G, C, D). I have chosen to use Cmaj7 chords most of the time to give the tune a prettier sound, but you could use a plain C chord as well. The melody moves along at a steady pace, which doesn't leave much room for simple arpeggio embellishment, so instead, try displacing bass notes as well as taking liberties with the melodic phrasing.

Introduction Suggestions

The pickup notes to measure 13 through the end of the tune provide a traditional introduction. A simple 3/4 picking pattern over a G chord, or G to D7, would also make a nice introduction.

Ending Suggestions

A simple ritard into the last two measures works effectively. For a more interesting ending when performing instrumentally, try replacing the final G chord with an Em, and then repeat either the last 4 measures (starting with the pickup notes from measure 12) or the last two measures starting with the pickup notes in measure 14.

Sample Recording

The example recording is fairly simple. I created an introduction with an arpeggio pattern on G, C, G, C, and then played the song once as written. On the second pass, I added arpeggios wherever there was room, and in a few places, slightly altered the phrasing of the melody. I added a ritard to the final two measures to end the song.

COME THOU FOUNT OF EVERY BLESSING

Robert Robinson/Anonymous
Arr. Doug Young

FAIREST LORD JESUS

Words: Anonymous
Music: Traditional

Fairest Lord Jesus, ruler of all nature,
O thou of God and man the Son,
Thee will I cherish, Thee will I honor,
Thou, my soul's glory, joy, and crown.

The origins of this song are unclear. It was first published in German in 1842. The melody is an older tune, sometimes referred to as the "Crusader's Hymn", which was rumored to have been sung by German Crusaders on their way to the Holy Land.

Performance Tips and Comments

This arrangement is in the key of A major, so, A, D, and E are the primary chords used. For a softer, prettier sound, most of the A chords could be changed to Amaj7. The Bm7 and C#m7 chords can be played as barre chords, offering more flexibility to add other chord voices, but I find them easier to play as indicated, fingering only the 2nd, 3rd, and 5th strings. You can even play these chords as shown in measure 13, with just two voices.

Introduction Suggestions

The final four measures, starting with the pickup note to measure 13, make a good introduction for singers. A simple arpeggio pattern over A and E, repeated as many times as you like, also works well. Another nice introduction sequence would be A, C#m7, Bm7, E.

Ending Suggestions

Repeating the last four bars as a tag ending works well. You can also simply ritard starting with measure 14.

Sample Recording

On the recording, I started with arpeggios over a first position Amaj7 chord and an Eadd9 chord. After the initial pass through the song, I began to add some additional arpeggiated notes to the longer held chords. For the ending, I made several adjustments. First, I played the second melody note of measure 13 (a C#) on the 3rd string, 6th fret, sliding up to the note. This felt a little smoother, and got my hand in position for the C#m7, which I played as a 3-note chord, as shown in the chord diagram. I changed the A chord in measure 14 to an Amaj7, and then played a long arpeggio over an Eadd9 chord – the same one I used in the introduction – before resolving to the final chord. For the final A chord, I played the 2nd string open, creating an Aadd9 chord.

Here is what I played for the introduction:

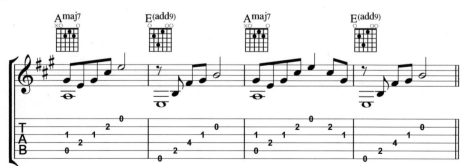

FAIREST LORD JESUS

Traditional
Arr. Doug Young

FAITH OF OUR FATHERS

Words: Frederick W. Faber (1849)
Music: Henri F. Hemy (1864)

Faith of our fathers! living still
In spite of dungeon, fire, and sword;
Oh, how our hearts beat high with joy
Whene'er we hear that glorious word!
Faith of our fathers, holy faith!
We will be true to thee till death!

Faith of Our Fathers was written as a tribute to Catholic martyrs under King Henry the VIII. The author wrote two versions of the hymn, one intended for an English audience, the other for the Irish. Like many hymns, the words are sung to alternate melodies. The melody of "St Catherine" is generally used in the United States.

Performance Tips and Comments

This arrangement is in the key of C, so the harmony involves mostly C, F, and G, along with a few relative minor chords. The F chord often presents a challenge when played as a full barre chord. In most cases, this arrangement can be played without barring by playing partial F chords. In measure 22, try playing the F chord by fretting the low F with your thumb.

Introduction Suggestions

Try playing arpeggios on C-F-C-G (I-IV-I-V). As always, the final four measures also makes a useful introduction.

Ending Suggestions

Ritarding on the last two measures works well on this song.

Sample Recording

The example recording consists of an introduction, two verses, and a tag ending. For the introduction, I used the last phrase, starting at measure 21, but with some variation. I fingered the Am chord as an Am9 at the fifth fret, allowing me to play the descending scale notes across the strings for a more harp-like sound. I ended the introduction on the G chord, with a simple arpeggio to lead into the first verse. The introduction on the recording goes like this:

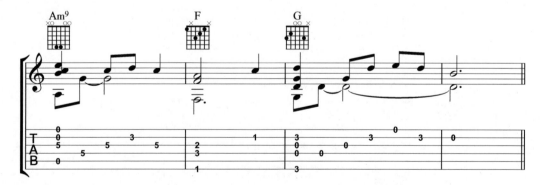

After playing two verses, one as written, the second with improvised variations, I ended by walking from the C chord in measure 24, down to an A, to pick up the Am to start a repeat of the final phrase. However, I again, fingered the Am as the same Am9 used in the intro.

FAITH OF OUR FATHERS

Frederick W. Faber/Henri F. Hemy
Arr. Doug Young

FOR THE BEAUTY OF THE EARTH

Words: Folliott Sandford Pierpoint (1864)
Music: Conrad Kocher (1838)

For the beauty of the earth,
for the glory of the skies,
for the love which from our birth
over and around us lies.

This song was inspired by the beauty of the countryside. The melody usually used is an older song, known as "DIX", after William Dix. Dix published a popular hymn based on the melody, which had been written earlier by Conrad Kocher.

Performance Tips and Comments

This is a simple song, in the key of C and only twelve measures long. The first and second lines of the song are identical. In spite of the simplicity, it can be a challenge to play slow fingerstyle tunes in the key of C, because of the barred F chord. To make it a bit easier to play smoothly, it can help to recognize that in measure 2, you don't need to hold all the strings down. You can finger a full barred F, but only need the bass note and top three strings. You could also simplify the F chord by playing the bass note on the 4th string, 3rd fret, eliminating the need to barre. I also followed the F chord with a Cmaj7, both because I like the prettier sound, and because it allows an easier transition from the F.

In measure 3, I avoid barring the F chord by playing only strings, 6, 4, and 3, followed by a voicing that used only strings 2, 3, and 4.

The last note of measure 11 is an F, played on the 1st string, 1st fret over an Am chord. You might prepare for this note by fingering the Am with a partial barre on strings 1 and 2.

Introduction Suggestions

This song is quite short, so consider either using any standard chord progression in the key of C, or the final two measures as an introduction.

Ending Suggestions

Doubling the length of the final three chords of measure 12 creates a good ending.

Sample Recording

For the sample recording, I played a chord pattern of C, F, C, G as an introduction before playing the song as written. After some minor embellishments on the second time through the tune, I substituted an Am for the final C chord, followed by an F, and finally repeated the last two measures, holding out the final three chords approximately twice as long as written.

FOR THE BEAUTY OF THE EARTH

Folliot Sandford Pierpoint/Conrad Kocher

arr. Doug Young

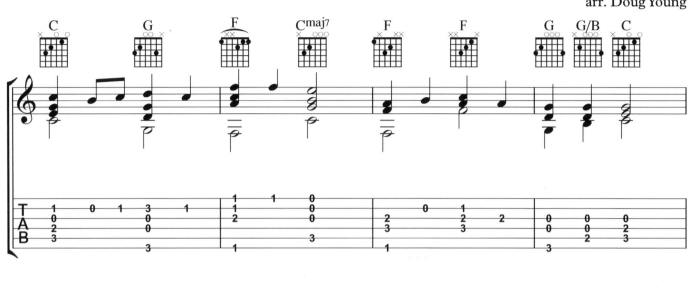

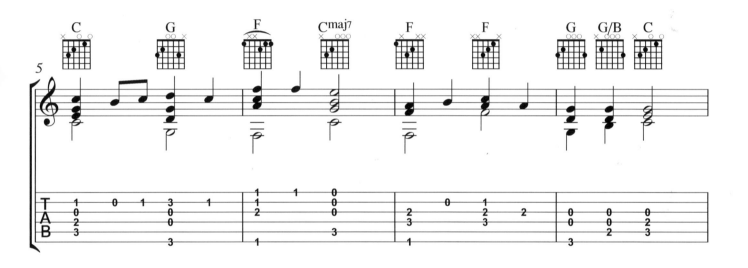

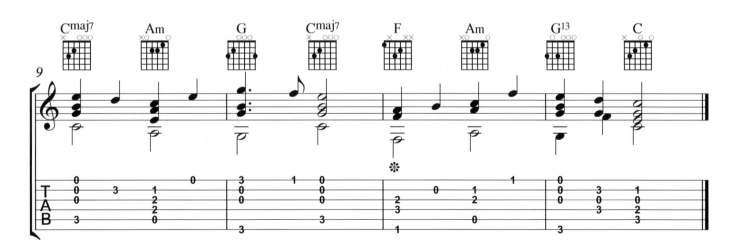

HE LEADETH ME

Words: Joseph H. Gilmore (1862)
Music: William B. Bradbury (1864)

He leadeth me: O blessed thought!
O words with heavenly comfort fraught!
Whate'er I do, where'er I be,
Still 'tis God's hand that leadeth me.

While many hymns are sung to multiple melodies, the poem He Leadeth Me inspired William Bradbury to write this melody specifically for the hymn.

Performance Tips and Comments

This is a mostly straightforward arrangement in the key of G. The melody moves along at a steady place, leaving less room for embellishment than some other hymns. The arrangement does depart from first position with the high A over a D chord in measures 10 and 14. Playing the preceding D chord using a partial barre will make it easier to play the A melody note smoothly with your pinky. An alternate fingering would be to play the D chord in the fifth position, as follows:

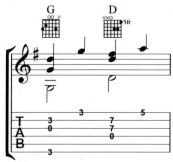

Notice the fingering of the G chord in measures 10 and 14. Fingering both the D on the 2nd string, 3rd fret and the G on the 1st string third fret makes it easier to play the melody smoothly and facilitates the move to the following D chord.

Introduction Suggestions

The last two measures act as a good introduction for singers. Alternately, a simple picking pattern over a G chord works well. Also consider a I-vi-ii-V progression (G, Em, Am, D).

Ending Suggestions

A tag ending using the last two measures (with the pickup in measure 14) is one option. Or simply ritard the final two measures.

Sample Recording

For this recording, I kept things extremely simple: no introduction, no special ending. I just played the tune twice, once as written, and again with some very minor elaborations.

HE LEADETH ME

Joseph H. Gilmore/William B. Bradbury
Arr. Doug Young

HOLY, HOLY, HOLY

Words: Reginald Heber (1826)
Music: John Dykes (1861)

Holy, holy, holy! Lord God Almighty!
Early in the morning our song shall rise to thee.
Holy, holy, holy! Merciful and mighty!
God in three Persons, blessed Trinity!

The song refers to the Trinity, and the melody was written as a tribute to the Council of Nicea that formalized the Trinity doctrine. Holy, Holy, Holy is well known, and has been used in a number of movies, from the 1953 film "Titanic" to a Glenn Ford western, "The Fastest Gun Alive".

Performance Tips and Comments

This arrangement uses simple chords in first position, and should not present any unique challenges. The tune can be played slowly, giving enough space for some embellishment between melody notes, especially on the half notes and whole notes.

Introduction Suggestions

You can use the last four bars as an introduction. Another idea is to start on a G, and use a descending bass to D: G, D/F#, Em, D.

Ending Suggestions

A simple ritard on the last two measures works well. Another idea would be to stretch the final two measures to be twice as long - going to "half time".

Sample Recording

The example recording demonstrates an introduction, two verses, and a tag ending. The introduction is based on the final four measures, outlining the harmony with a descending melody line. The idea was to hint at the tune by using the harmony and some of the melody notes without simply playing the final phase. The introduction on the recording is:

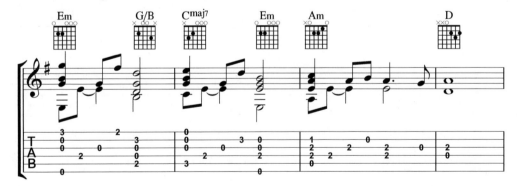

The ending simply repeats the final four measures, ritarding on the final beats.

HOLY, HOLY, HOLY

Reginald Heber / John Dykes
Arr. Doug Young

I HAVE DECIDED TO FOLLOW JESUS

Words: Anonymous
Music: Traditional

I have decided to follow Jesus;
I have decided to follow Jesus;
I have decided to follow Jesus;
No turning back, no turning back.

This hymn is of unknown origin, although there is a legend that it was sung by a man in India who had, along with his family, been converted to Christianity. His family was killed for their faith, while he refused to recant his religion and continued to sing. The melody is known as Assam, which is the name of the region of India where the hymn originated.

Performance Tips and Comments

This is a simple tune and quite short - only eight bars long, so the challenge in performing it as a solo instrumental is to make it interesting through variations. The core arrangement is written using mostly alternating bass, but you might try some other bass patterns as well. For example, try just playing the root of each chord with a dotted-quarter/eighth note rhythm. Harmonies can also be altered. Try substituting relative minors for most major chords - G becomes Em, C becomes Am and so on. Both the G and C chords could be played as major 7th chords as well, for a prettier sound.

Introduction Suggestions

The final phase, starting with the pickup notes to measure 8, works as an introduction. You might also consider just starting with alternate bass notes (4th and 6th strings) on a G chord.

Ending Suggestions

Repeat the final phrase starting with the pickup notes to measure 8, then simply ritard on the final two measures, or continue to vamp on an alternating bass in G for a few measures.

Sample Recording

For this tune, I took a slightly different approach from the formula I've used to demonstrate most of these hymns. I began by playing some harmonics that approximate the initial phrase of the melody, as follows:

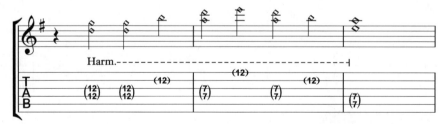

From there, I played the melody alone with no accompaniment, trying to let the notes ring as much as possible. There are a couple of ways to accomplish this. For example, most of the melody notes to this song can be played directly out of a (partially) barred G chord on the third fret. However, I chose to use as many open strings as I could, basically following the top line of the music as written. If you like this single-note approach, experiment with different fingerings and locations on the fretboard to get different effects. On the recording, I then played the second verse as written. The final pass through the song is almost exactly as written, except that I added a subtle rhythmic pulse to the bass line by adding an extra eighth note before the bass note on beat three. For an ending, I repeated the final phrase – the pickup notes at the end of measure 7 – and played a ritard into the final G chord.

I HAVE DECIDED TO FOLLOW JESUS

Anonymous
Arr. Doug Young

IN THE GARDEN

Words and Music: C. Austin Miles (1912)

I come to the garden alone,
While the dew is still on the roses;
And the voice I hear, falling on my ear,
The Son of God discloses.

In the Garden, also known as I Come to the Garden Alone, was made popular by the Billy Sunday evangelist campaigns. It has been recorded by Roy Rogers and Dale Evans, Tennessee Ernie Ford and many others.

Performance Tips and Comments

Like many tunes in 6/8 time, this song is best felt as triplets in 2/4 time. I've chosen major 7th chords for C when the melody notes allow - for example in measure 2. Some of the F chords could also be played as major 7ths. All G chords could have an added 7th as well. The F chords could be played as barre chords, but you have a bit more flexibility if you can play the root with your thumb.

Introduction Suggestions

A 6/8 (or 3/4) picking pattern of C, F and G would make a simple intro. To accompany singers, start with the last beat of measure 12 and play the last four measures.

Ending Suggestions

Simply ritard and end on C, or continue with arpeggios over C, F and back to C.

Sample Recording

The recording is very simple, with no added introduction or ending. I simply played once as written, and again with small elaborations.

IN THE GARDEN

C. Austin Miles
Arr. Doug Young

Jesus Loves Me

Words: Anna Bartlett Warner (1859)
Music: William B. Bradbury (1861)

Jesus loves me, this I know,
For the Bible tells me so.
Little ones to him belong;
They are weak, but he is strong.

Jesus Loves Me is usually viewed as a children's song, and is perhaps one of the most well-known hymns.

Performance Tips and Comments

This is a simple tune in the key of C, so the chords are primarily C, F, and G, along with Em and Am. C's and G's can often be played as either triads or major 7ths. You could skip the faster-moving bass notes starting in measure 9, but these add a little motion to the chorus of the song.

Introduction Suggestions

For accompanying singers, the pickup to the last two measures works well, and you could optionally go to a D7 chord to cue the singers. For a solo instrumental, you might simply start playing without an introduction. The descending bass used in the first two bars of this arrangement also suggests an introduction, playing G, G/F#, Em, and D7.

Ending Suggestions

You could end by stretching the final eighth notes in measure 15 out to two beats each, creating a dramatic ritard. You might also use the pickup note to the final two measures as a "tag" ending, repeated one or more times.

Sample Recording

The sample recording performs the song twice, once as written, and then with some elaborations and variations. I repeated the final two measures to create an ending.

JESUS LOVES ME

Anna Bartlett Warner/William B. Bradbury
arr. Doug Young

JESUS, KEEP ME NEAR THE CROSS

Words: Fanny Crosby (1869)
Music: W. Howard Doane

Jesus, keep me near the cross,
There a precious fountain;
Free to all, a healing stream,
Flows from Calv'ry's mountain.

This song is different from many hymns in that William Howard Doane wrote the melody first, and Fanny Crosby added the lyrics later.

Performance Tips and Comments

This tune is sometimes written in a tuple meter, 6/8, 3/4 or 6/4. However, for a solo performance, I felt like it flowed more smoothly in 4/4 time, as it is written here. The arrangement falls entirely in the first position in the key of G, and uses basic key of G chords: G, C, D, Em and Am.

Introduction Suggestions

The typical church piano introduction would consist of the final two measures. An arpeggiated G, C, G, D would also work well.

Ending Suggestions

Consider holding the Em at the end of measure 14 for a bit, then playing the final two measures, ritarding into the final G chord. You might also repeat these final two measures again as an ending.

Sample Recording

For the recording, I created an introduction inspired by the opening notes: B, C, B. I played a simple lick using those two notes over a G chord, repeated it over a CMaj7, again over G, then to a D, leading into the melody.

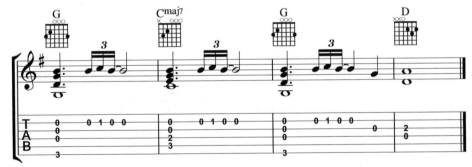

As usual, the first verse is played as written, while the second time through I played more freely, adding embellishments. For an ending, I simply repeated the final two measures, slowing down into the final G chord.

JESUS, KEEP ME NEAR THE CROSS

Fanny Crosby/W. Howard Doane
Arr. Doug Young

JUST AS I AM

Words: Charlotte Elliott (1835)
Music: "Woodworth" William B. Bradbury (1849)

Just as I am, without one plea
But that Thy blood was shed for me
And that Thou bid'st me come to Thee
O Lamb of God, I come! I come.

Hearing this song prompted Billy Graham to first convert to Christianity, and remained as his alter call song for his crusades. It was also the title of his autobiography.

Performance Tips and Comments

This song has an unusual structure, being 18 bars long. It is sometimes written in 6/4 time, which ends up being nine measures long. The repeated occurrences of half-notes and dotted quarter notes provide opportunities to add arpeggiated accompaniment between the melody notes.

Introduction Suggestions

To accompany singers, you could start an introduction with the pickup notes at the end of bar 12. Or try a simple chord sequence of G, Em, C, D.

Ending Suggestions

Try repeating the final phrase starting with bar 15.

Sample Recording

My recording of Just As I Am starts with a short four-chord introduction inspired by the final two chords of the song, but in reverse. I play G, D/F#, Em, and C before launching into the initial verse as written:

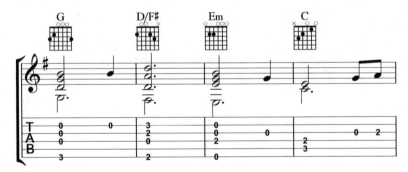

For the second verse, I stayed close to the written music, but played more freely and added bass notes and arpeggios where I could.

For the final verse, I was feeling brave and departed from the chord shapes in the initial phrase. Instead of sticking to the chord shapes, I played the melody entirely on the 3rd string. This was fairly easy to do, since I only needed to finger the G bass at the beginning and end of the phrase, and could use the open 6th string for the bass note in the second measure, and open 4th string for the D in the third measure. By sliding around the 3rd string for the melody notes, I created a very different texture. To take liberties like this – at least on the fly – you need to know the melody well, and it also helps to know the notes of the fretboard as well as chord shapes higher up the neck. For example, I played the phrase starting at measure 9 the same way, but was able to grab a CMaj7 in third position in measure 11 instead of the 1st position C chord that is written in the music.

To end the song, I looped back to the final three chords, repeating the D, D/F#, G starting in measure 15.

JUST AS I AM

Charlotte Elliot/William B. Bradbury
Arr. Doug Young

LOVE LIFTED ME

Words: James Rowe (1912)
Music: Howard E. Smith (1912)

Love lifted me! Love lifted me!
When nothing else could help,
Love lifted me.

Love Lifted Me was written by James Rowe, and was inspired by several stories in the Bible where Jesus and the disciples are out on the water. The song was recorded by Kenny Rogers for his first solo album of the same name.

Performance Tips and Comments

This song is usually sung somewhat enthusiastically, with a march-like cadence and bounce. It's written in 6/8 time, and generally feels like it is in "2". I've kept the bass notes simple, one per measure, which allows some flexibility in your interpretation. If you want to play it more up-tempo, consider doubling up on the bass notes, playing notes on every dotted-quarter down beat. For example, here is the first line, with the harmony simplified and adding steady bass notes.

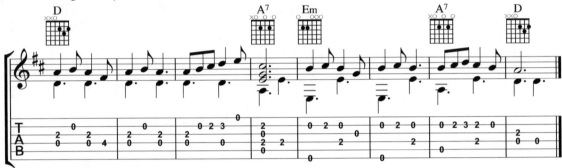

However, you could also create a more leisurely interpretation of the tune.

Introduction Suggestions

To accompany singers, you could start with the final three eighth notes at the end of measure 21 and take the second ending. The G/B to A13 in measure 25 would also make a simple introduction. If you are playing the tune more up-tempo, you might also start with an alternating bass pattern on D.

Ending Suggestions

It's common to hold out the notes in the second ending, measure 25, basically doubling the length before resolving the D chord at the end.

Sample Recording

The recording begins with a simple introduction consisting of D to A7. After one pass as written, and a second with embellishments, I arpeggiated the D chord in measure 26, then repeated the final two measures more slowly to end the song.

LOVE LIFTED ME

James Rowe/Howard E. Smith
Arr. Doug Young

PRAISE HIM, PRAISE HIM

Words: Fanny Crosby (1869)
Music: Chester G. Allen (1869)

Praise him! praise him! Jesus, our blessed Redeemer!
Sing, O earth his wonderful love proclaim!
Hail him! hail him! highest archangels in glory,
Strength and honor give to his holy name!

Praise Him, Praise Him is one of Fanny Crosby's best known tunes. Fanny Crosby wrote over 8000 hymns during her lifetime. To avoid problems with publishers who might be reluctant to produce hymn books that were dominated by Crosby's songs, she used over 200 pseudonyms.

Performance Tips and Comments

This song is often sung fairly quickly and triumphantly, but as an instrumental, it could be played slower and more expressively. The tune is in 6/8 time, and should be counted in "2", with the eighth notes felt as triplets. Because the melody moves along fairly rapidly, I've reduced the number of chord tones used throughout the arrangement. The diagrams indicate the full chord shapes that are implied, and it may be helpful to finger the full chords - or at least visualize them as you play. However, the song sounds less ponderous with fewer notes in the chords, and so most of the written arrangement consists of just a melody against bass notes, with an occasional extra chord voice. You may want to finger the full chord shapes to support embellishments in many places.

Introduction Suggestions

The standard introduction phrase for accompanying singers starts at measure 29. You could also try a 6/8 (triplet) picking pattern over various chord progressions in the key of G. For example, try repeating G and Em a few times, or G, Em, C, D.

Ending Suggestions

This song lends itself to a tag ending - repeat the final four bars slightly more slowly.

Sample Recording

I kept the example recording very basic, with just two verses and no introduction. For the ending, I simply slowed down dramatically from measure 30 to the end. The melody to this song is very busy leaving little room for embellishment. On the second time through, I basically tried to add 6/8 arpeggios to some of the longer held chords. You could interpret the song differently, playing it much slower, which would allow more opportunities for variations.

PRAISE HIM, PRAISE HIM

Fanny Crosby/Chester G. Allen
Arr. Doug Young

SWEET HOUR OF PRAYER

Words: W. W. Walford (1845)
Music: William B. Bradbury (1861)

Sweet hour of prayer! sweet hour of prayer!
That calls me from a world of care,
And bids me at my Father's throne
Make all my wants and wishes known.

William Walford was a blind English preacher. Bradbury wrote a melody for Walford's poem several years after it was first published.

Performance Tips and Comments

This tune is fairly straightforward, and is in the key of G in 3/4 time. It lends itself to a fairly slow, expressive treatment. The diminished chord in measure 28 could be fingered in a number of different ways, but the fingering indicated here is fairly simple, and creates the diminished sound with the melody note on top.

Introduction Suggestions

For the standard hymnal introduction, start with the last note in measure 28, but play the melody note only, then proceed to the end.

Ending Suggestions

For a tag ending, consider repeating the final eight measures, starting with the pickup note in measure 24, or the final four measures starting with the last note in measure 28.

Sample Recording

The example recording has no special introduction. After the second time through the song, I ended by repeating the final four measures.

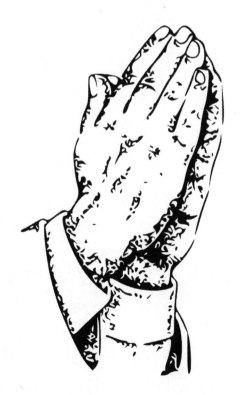

SWEET HOUR OF PRAYER

W. W. Walford / William B. Bradbury
Arr. Doug Young

THE OLD RUGGED CROSS

Words and Music: George Bennard (1912)

So I'll cherish the old rugged cross
Till my trophies at last I lay down
And I will cling to the old rugged cross
And exchange it some day for a crown.

Written by George Bennard in 1912, The Old Rugged Cross has the distinction of its first complete performance being accompanied by a guitar. It has been widely recorded by country artists including Patsy Cline, Loretta Lynn, The Statler Brothers, Merle Haggard, and many more.

Performance Tips and Comments

This arrangement is in the key of G, and presents a few challenges. This is an example of a tune where I violated my original goal of staying in first position, and involves a few sections fairly high on the fretboard. Even before we get to that, pay attention to the fingering suggested in measures 1 and 3, where the melody introduces some accidentals that don't lay as well under the fingers.

The melody requires a move out of first position for the high C on the eighth fret in measure 14. Moving smoothly to the high note is facilitated by playing the Am using only a partial barre, leaving an open A string. Note the D7 chord in measure 17, which allows us to play the chord with a high A on top. The end of measure 24 starts a big leap up to the 7th position. I would slide up to the D on the 7th fret, third string with my first finger.

Playing a G chord with a high B represents an arrangement problem. You might be able to reach the G bass note on the 3rd fret, 6th string, while playing the high B on the 1st string, 7th fret, but it's a stretch. Instead, I'm playing the lowest note on the open 3rd string. The chord sounds thinner, but it still works. There's another big jump between the high G chord in measure 26, back down to the Cmaj7 in measure 27, then back up to the melody notes on the eighth fret in measure 28.

All in all, this tune should give you a chance to work on moving freely around the fretboard!

Once you have the basic tune under your fingers, there are a lot of variations possible with this tune. For example you might find it both more interesting, and possibly easier to play the opening lines, by harmonizing the melody in thirds, like this:

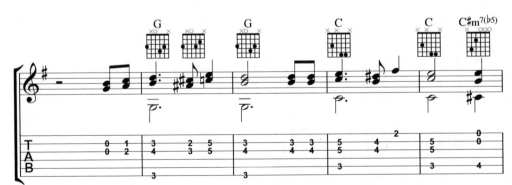

This hymn is a bit trickier to play smoothly than most of the songs in this book, between the unusual accidentals in the melody and the frequent jumps around the fretboard, so take your time and work out the fingerings as well as your ideas for embellishments.

The long notes in measure 19 offer an opportunity to add a fill. Try something like this lick:

In measure 18, a nice variation is to harmonize the melody in 6ths, creating a descending bass line, like this:

Introduction Suggestions
To accompany singers, you might start with the pickup notes in measure 28.

Ending Suggestions
One possible ending would be to simply ritard in measure 30, and perhaps end with G, C, G.

Sample Recording
In the example recording, I played a simple introduction consisting of just a fingerpicking pattern over G, C, G. After playing the verse as written, the second pass uses some of the ideas outlined above, along with some additional arpeggiation and general embellishments. For the ending, I played the final G chord, before going to a C/G for a moment, then jumped back up the the high C on the eight fret, to repeat the last four bars. This time, instead of landing on the first position G chord in measure 31, I played a descending G arpeggio in the 7th position, followed by an ascending C major arpeggio, followed by the final C chord, breaking out of the 3/4 feel. Here's what I played on the ending:

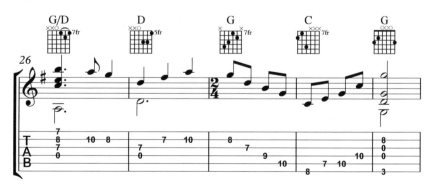

THE OLD RUGGED CROSS

George Bennard
Arr. Doug Young

THE OLD RUGGED CROSS

THIS IS MY FATHER'S WORLD

Words: Maltbie D. Babcock (1901)
Music: Traditional

This is my Father's world,
And to my listening ears
All nature sings, and round me rings
The music of the spheres.

This poem was published after the author's death in 1901, and later set to the music of a traditional English melody by a friend, Franklin Sheppard. The melody has been used in The Lord of the Rings, Ken Burns' film The National Parks, and even Penn Jillette's "Penn's Sunday School" podcast.

Performance Tips and Comments

This tune could be harmonized more simply, but I've tried to introduce some chord substitutions to make it more harmonically interesting without being dramatically different. Many of the minor chords could be replaced by their relative majors for some variety. For example, the Em in measure 2 could be replaced by a G major and the Am in measure 3 could be played as simply a C major chord. I've also used Cmaj7 frequently, to produce a softer, prettier sound.

Introduction Suggestions

For a standard hymn-like introduction, start with the pickup note in measure 12. A simple vamp with a descending bass line (G, G/F#, Em, D) would also work well as an introduction.

Ending Suggestions

The same descending bass vamp suggested for the intro, G, G/F#, Em, D, then back to G, would make a nice ending. You could create a tag ending from either the last four measures (with the pickup note in measure 12) or the final 2 measures, with the pickup note in measure 14.

Sample Recording

For the sample recording, I used a capo on the second fret, so the song sounds as if it is in A. I created an introduction based around the initial pickup notes of the melody, alternating between G and Cmaj7, ending on D, like this:

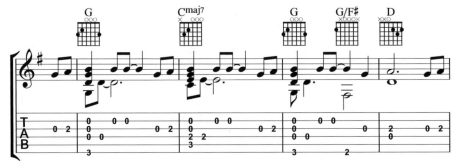

I played one verse as written, then a second adding embellishments and taking some liberties with the timing and phrasing. For an ending, I replaced the final G chord with a Cmaj7 chord and then repeated the last phrase. This is similar to the relative minor trick I used on several of these recordings, but using the IV chord instead.

THIS IS MY FATHER'S WORLD

Maltbie D. Babcock/Traditional
Arr. Doug Young

TURN YOUR EYES UPON JESUS

Words and Music: Helen Howarth Lemmel (1918)

Turn your eyes upon Jesus
Look full in His wonderful face
And the things of earth will grow strangely dim
In the light of His glory and grace

This song is also known as "The Heavenly Vision." The country music singer, Alan Jackson recorded the song for his father-in-law's funeral.

Performance Tips and Comments

This tune has some interesting chromaticism, starting with the A#/Bb in the first measure, as well as some interesting harmonies, especially the move from C major to C minor in measure 28. Overall, the tune should be easy to play, and lays comfortably mostly in first position in the key of G.

Introduction Suggestions

The typical approach of using the last phrase starts on the last beat of measure 24. A 3/4 picking pattern over a simple G, C and D progression would also work well.

Ending Suggestions

The last time through, consider holding the dramatic-sounding Cm in measure 28 a bit longer, and then finish with a ritard to the ending.

Sample Recording

For the sample recording, I used a capo at the second fret, making the song sound in the key of A, and giving it a slightly more delicate sound. I added an introduction based on Gmaj7 and Cmaj7 back and forth, ending on a D. Here's what I played:

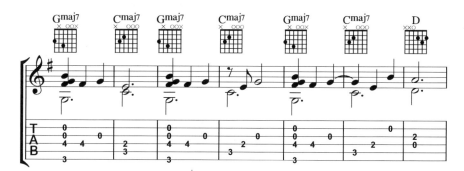

After the introduction, I played the song twice, once as written, and the second time with minor embellishments. When I reached the end of the second pass, I played a basic first position Em instead of the final G, followed by a first position A, before repeating the final phrase starting with the pickup notes at the end of measure 28. This is the same trick used in several other recordings for this book – replacing the last chord with its relative minor before repeating the last phase – but with the addition of a secondary dominant (the A) before repeating the ending phrase.

TURN YOUR EYES UPON JESUS

Helen Howarth Lemmel
Arr. Doug Young

TURN YOUR EYES UPON JESUS

WE ARE CLIMBING JACOB'S LADDER

Words and Music: Traditional Spiritual (Circa 1750-1825)

We are climbing Jacob's ladder
We are climbing Jacob's ladder
We are climbing Jacob's ladder
Soldiers of the cross.

This is an African American spiritual that was sung by slaves as a call-and-response type of song.

Performance Tips and Comments

Short, simple tunes like this present a challenge when played instrumentally. To keep the song interesting over multiple verses, you'll want to introduce some variations. One idea for variations can come from the call-and-response style in which the song is often sung: "We are (we are) climbing (climbing) Jacob's (Jacob's) Ladder" and so on. I have not written any responses into the arrangement, but you can easily add them in various ways. For example, you could create an "answer" in each measure using bass notes:

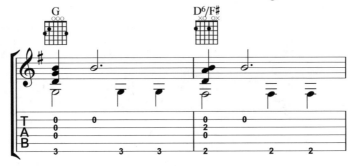

Or you could create an answer effect with notes from the chord, as follows. There are many other possibilities.

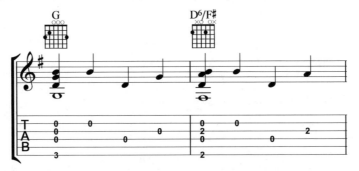

Sample Recording

I started the recording by playing the melody of the last four measures using (mostly) harmonics, as follows:

I followed this by a rhythm on a low G to set the mood. The first verse is played as written, followed by two verses using the suggestions described above. I ended by repeating the final four measures, slowing down into the final chord.

WE ARE CLIMBING JACOB'S LADDER

Traditional Spiritual
Arr. Doug Young

WHAT A FRIEND WE HAVE IN JESUS

Words: Joseph Scriven (1855)
Music: Charles Converse (1868)

What a friend we have in Jesus,
All our sins and griefs to bear!
What a privilege to carry
Everything to God in prayer!

Joseph Scriven composed this poem for his mother. The melody that is typically used was composed by Charles Converse and first published in 1870.

Performance Tips and Comments

This arrangement should be fairly easy, and lays well in the key of A in first position. Watch for the fingering of the D chord in measure 2. If it's hard to play the bass note on the 5th string, you could just play the melody note (F#). There are some alternate approaches to some sections of this tune that you may want to try. For example, try playing the first two measures in the fifth position, to leverage some open strings, as follows:

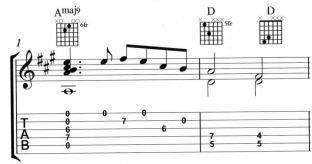

This creates a rich Amaj9 sound. This tune sounds nice with prettier chords in many places. For example, consider bars 11 and 12. You could play them as follows, with major 7ths and add 9 chords:

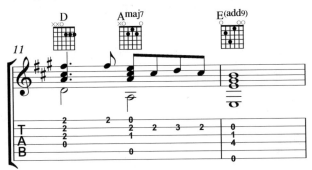

Sample Recording

For the recording, I used a capo on the 2nd fret, raising the effective key to B. The introduction consists of an Amaj7 to an Eadd9, repeated twice. After the second verse, I repeated the final two measures, but harmonized the melody in thirds for the ending, as follows:

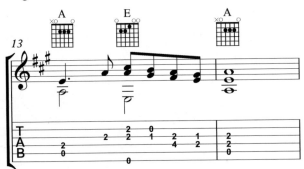

64

WHAT A FRIEND WE HAVE IN JESUS

Joseph Scriven/Charles Converse
Arr. Doug Young

WHISPERING HOPE

Words and Music: Septimus Winner (1868)

Soft as the voice of an angel,
Breathing a lesson unheard,
Hope with a gentle persuasion
Whispers her comforting word

Septimus Winner was a prolific composer and arranger. Whispering Hope has been recorded by Jim Reeves, Willie Nelson, and many others.

Performance Tips and Comments

This arrangement should be straightforward, but has more measures than most of the other tunes in this book. A bit of attention to fingering will make chord changes smoother. For example, I'd suggest playing the initial G chord with your 3rd finger on the 2nd string, 3rd fret, allowing you to just play the high G of the next chord with your 4th finger. Although the tune is in the key of G, there are a few chromatic passages - such as measure 18 - and some more complex harmonies, such as the secondary dominant, A9, in measure 21 that may require some attention to fingering.

The B section on the second page has a sort of answering line in each phrase. Try to hold out the top melody note, while playing the rhythmic pattern on the middle strings in each phase.

Measure 39 goes up to a high B on the 1st string, 7th fret. Ideally, we'd use a full G chord here, but to make the arrangement easier to play, I'm using a G/B chord, with no root.

The song is in 3/4 time, and there are many dotted half notes that provide opportunities to add fill notes, connecting bass lines, and arpeggiated harmonies.

Introduction Suggestions

For a typical hymn introduction, start four measures from the end, and conclude on a D or D7 to lead into the beginning of the tune. You might also play any common chord progression in the key of G.

Ending Suggestions

You could simply ritard on the final phrase. Alternately, repeat the final two measures.

Sample Recording

The sample recording has no introduction, and I just played the song twice, once as written, and the second time adding a few embellishments. Upon reaching the end of the second chorus, I repeated the last line, starting with measure 45, slowing down as I reach the final chord.

WHISPERING HOPE

Septimus Winner
Arr. Doug Young

WHISPERING HOPE

ABOUT THE AUTHOR

Doug Young is fingerstyle guitarist, composer, performer and author who lives in the San Francisco Bay Area. He is a Contributing Editor to Acoustic Guitar Magazine and the author of the best-selling Mel Bay book, *Understanding DADGAD for Fingerstyle Guitar* as well as *Fiddle Tunes for DADGAD, A DADGAD Christmas* and *Acoustic Guitar Amplification Essentials* (String Letter Publishing). He has released multiple CDs of original music and arrangements, *Laurel Mill* and *Closing Time,* which are available with accompanying transcriptions, *DUETS,* a collection of fingerstyle duets with Teja Gerken, and *Forever Christmas,* arrangements of instrumental Christmas music featuring acoustic guitar as well as violin, viola, cello and recorder/flute.

This book is part of a series. Volume 2, *Christmas Carols for Fingerstyle Guitar,* and Volume 3, *MORE Hymns for Fingerstyle Guitar,* follow the same philosophy and approach with additional arrangements.

For comments or questions about this book, contact the author at:

doug@dougyoungguitar.com

Books are available through Amazon.com and MelBay.com. CDs and tablature are available from the author's website:

http://www.dougyoungguitar.com

OTHER BOOKS BY DOUG YOUNG
AVAILABLE ON AMAZON.COM

MORE Hymns for Fingerstyle Guitar is the third volume in the Fingerstyle Fakebook Series. The book follows the same style and format as this book, and contains twenty-five additional classic hymns, arranged for guitar in standard tuning.

Christmas Carols for Fingerstyle Guitar is the second volume in the Fingerstyle Fakebook Series. The book follows the same style and format as this book, and contains twenty-five classic Christmas carols, arranged for guitar in standard tuning.

A DADGAD Christmas offers a collection of Christmas carols arranged for solo instrumental guitar in DADGAD tuning. The book is split into two sections. The first follows a similar format to this book - easy to play, single-page arrangements that you can sight-read and use as the basis of improvised elaborations. The second part of the book provides full-length fingerstyle arrangements in DADGAD tuning.

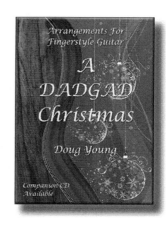

Understanding DADGAD is an instructional book designed to introduce this popular alternate tuning. The book starts from the beginning, progressing through chords, scales, melodic exercises and more. Two hundred examples provide a solid foundation for you to explore this tuning and create your own arrangements.

Made in the USA
Las Vegas, NV
05 November 2024

11170436R00039